Tales from Wales
6

D1550187

The Red Dragon of Wales

Myrddin ap Dafydd

Translated by Siân Lewis
Illustrated by Robin Lawrie

The Red Dragon is an impressive flag, don't you think? Most countries in the world have patterns on their flags, but the Welsh flag has a legendary creature and a plant. This is the oldest national flag in the world.

The white and green on the Welsh flag are the colours of the leek. The leek has been the national plant of Wales ever since Welsh soldiers wore leeks on their clothes, when they went to fight against the English army long ago. The leeks helped the Welshmen to recognise each other in the heat of battle. The Welsh won that battle and, ever since then, we have had great affection for the leek. The uniforms of the Welsh armies were once white and green too.

The legendary creature on the flag is, of course, the red dragon, and this book tells the story of that dragon. The two pictures merge to give the red, white and green of the Welsh – the flag that inspires us all, from sportsmen to poets and singers.

Many centuries ago, the Welsh lived in those areas we now call England and southern Scotland. There were no English people at that time, and the language spoken by everyone, from Edinburgh to London, was Old Welsh!

Gwrtheyrn, known as Vortigern in English, was

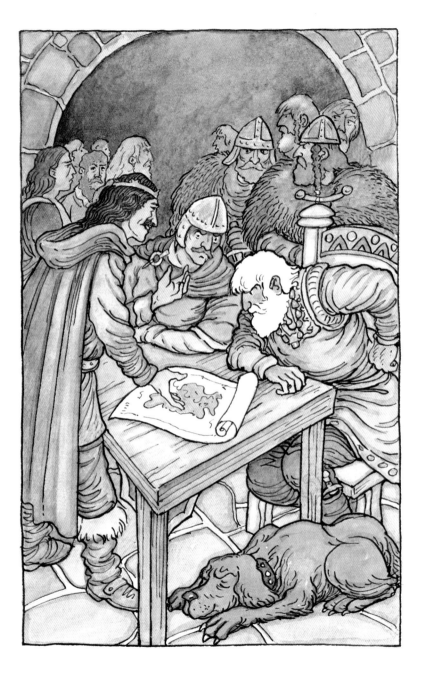

one of the kings of the Welsh long ago, and during his lifetime he had to fight constantly against armies who were trying to steal his land. In the end Gwrtheyrn asked a gang of madcap soldiers from northern Germany to help him. The names of their leaders were Hors and Hengist. These two were so dangerous they had been driven out of their own country.

With their help, Gwrtheyrn managed to hang on to his land – but, when the fighting was done, what could he do with Hors and Hengist and their unruly mob? In the end he decided to give them some poor marshy land in the south-east of England as a reward for their help. These were the first Saxons, and Gwrtheyrn is blamed for giving them their first foothold on these islands.

Soon the Saxons weren't satisfied with the land that had been given them, and went looking for more.

The Saxons invited king Gwrtheyrn and three hundred leaders of the Old Welsh to a banquet in one of their splendid halls. The Welsh set off in their best clothes, thanked the Saxons for their welcome and left their arms outside the hall. In the middle of the banquet, one of the Saxons shouted, "Grab your sax!" The 'sax' was the long knife that each member

of Hors and Hengist's mob carried with him. The Saxons grabbed their knives and launched a brutal attack on the leaders of the Old Welsh. The three hundred brave men were all killed. That night has been known to the Welsh ever since as 'The Treachery of the Long Knives'.

Gwrtheyrn's life was spared – but only because he agreed to give the whole of southern England to the Saxons. In addition, he had to leave his fine castle and most of his wealth, and flee for his life.

But where could he go? One thing was certain, he had to get as far away as possible from southern England and the dangerous mob that had settled there. He wanted to feel safe. He travelled for many long days and at last reached the mountains of Snowdonia in the north of our little country. He felt happier as soon as those mighty rocks closed around him.

Gwrtheyrn decided he would like to live in the mountains. Being a king, he had to build himself a castle, of course. He chose a steep slope near Beddgelert and ordered his architect and craftsmen to start work.

"The castle must be strong," he told them. "But it's also important to build it quickly, because my family and I have nowhere to live at present. I shall

give each one of you a generous reward, if you finish the work before winter."

The men set to work with a will. By the end of the very first day, the walls had already reached a fair height.

But next morning, the architect and the workers were horrified to find all their hard work of the previous day lying in ruins. The walls had collapsed, and some of the stones had rolled right down to the foot of the hill.

"This is very strange," said the architect. "But don't let's waste time. Start rebuilding the walls at once."

Throughout the day the craftsmen worked hard to rebuild the castle. By sunset the walls were even higher than the day before.

"Well done," said the architect. "We can all sleep soundly tonight."

But the following day, it was the same story all over again. Not a single stone was left standing – the walls had completely collapsed.

"We must rebuild the walls yet again," said the architect in bewilderment. "But tonight we'll sleep in tents on the hill, so we can see what mischief is at work, destroying our castle."

The men rebuilt the walls, and slept the night

in their tents. But their sleep was disturbed. In the middle of the night they heard a terrifying noise that made the earth tremble beneath them. When the men woke at dawn, their walls were lying in ruins once more.

On the third day, King Gwrtheyrn came to inspect the building site. His face fell when he saw the rubble.

"Where is my fine castle?" he cried. "I thought you'd have made more progress than this!"

Before the king could accuse the workmen of being lazy good-for-nothings, the architect rushed up to tell him what had happened.

"That's very strange, very strange indeed," said Gwrtheyrn. Were the Saxons still on his trail, he wondered. No, surely they wouldn't have followed him to the heart of Snowdonia. But who or what was causing this damage?

"We must call the wise men and ask their advice," he announced.

The wise men considered the facts at great length and scratched their heads all day.

"Well, what's the explanation?" the king asked impatiently.

"Er . . . um . . . perhaps there's an evil spirit living on the hill and interfering with the work,"

suggested one wise man.

"How can we get rid of him then?" was the king's next question.

"With great difficulty, O King, great difficulty. We must give the evil spirit a gift."

"What do you suggest?"

"A boy – a boy born without a father . . ."

"But that's impossible!" snorted the king. "Where could we find such a boy?"

"Every mountain and valley must be searched till the boy is found," said the wise man. "Then he must be brought here and killed, and his blood poured over the foundations of the castle. That's the only way to appease the evil spirit and build the walls safely."

"A reward!" announced Gwrtheyrn in a booming voice. "The first person to find me a boy born without a father will have his own weight in gold!"

When they heard the king's announcement, the workmen began to chatter excitedly amongst themselves. Where on earth would they find such a boy? Groups of bold men ventured along the most remote paths and travelled to every corner of the land.

It was a long and anxious wait for the king,

but at the end of that summer groups of tired men began to straggle back to the mountains of Snowdonia. They were all miserable and dejected. No one had managed to find the boy born without a father.

At the beginning of winter, when the mountaintops were white with snow, Gwrtheyrn and his camp were woken one morning by a shout from one of the sentries.

"A rider approaching from the south! A rider approaching from the south!"

Everyone stumbled out of their tents and looked down towards the path that led south. They could see a rider coming towards them. Some rubbed their eyes and looked again . . . and now they made out a small boy sitting in the saddle with the rider's arm wrapped tightly around him.

By this time there was high excitement in the camp. The rider reached them at last and announced, "Here he is! Here's the boy born without a father!"

"Are you sure?" asked Gwrtheyrn.

"Yes, O King. In Carmarthen town I saw two boys playing ball, and heard them quarrelling. One was making fun of the other because he had never had a father. This is the boy!"

"What is your name, my boy?" asked Gwrtheyrn.

"Myrddin Emrys," replied the lad. "And I know you want to kill me."

"How do you know that?" asked the king in astonishment.

"Oh, I know many things," replied the boy. "But believe me – you won't solve your problems by pouring my blood on the foundations of your castle. Who told you such a thing?"

"Those men over there, my wise men," said Gwrtheyrn.

"They are fools!" said the boy.

When they heard the boy call them fools, the wise men decided it was time to silence him. One of them approached Gwrtheyrn.

"The best plan is to kill him immediately and then you can start rebuilding your castle. There's no time to lose. We must appease the evil spirit."

"Huh! There is no evil spirit!" shouted the boy. "They're only guessing. They know nothing. But I know lots."

"What do you know, boy?" demanded Gwrtheyrn. "Do you know the secret of these stone walls?"

"I do," replied Myrddin Emrys. "In the heart of

that hill there's a cave and in the cave there's a lake. In the lake there are two dragons — a red dragon and a white dragon. Every night a fight takes place between the two dragons — a fierce fight that makes the earth shake. And as the earth shakes, your castle walls always fall down before morning."

"Rubbish! That's just a fairy story!" said the wise man.

"Dig into the side of the hill," challenged Myrddin Emrys. "You'll soon find the cave."

"King, we must kill this lad at once . . ." began the wise man.

"No!" insisted Gwrtheyrn. "I'm willing to give him a chance. Workmen! Start digging into the side of the hill."

Secretly the king was beginning to like the boy. He was obviously brave and quite fearless. He'd even dared to call the wise men fools! That took some courage. And yet not one of the wise men had managed to turn him into a bat or a mule for his rudeness. So Gwrtheyrn was beginning to think that maybe the boy was cleverer than they were after all.

A huge gang of workmen, armed with shovels, picks and levers, climbed up the hill. They began to

dig. And dig. And dig.

With each shovelful of soil that was removed from the hole in the slope, the wise men's shoulders grew straighter and their smiles broader. Well? Where were the cave and the lake and the dragons? There was no sign of them.

Then, "A hole!" shouted one of the workmen.

"It's more than a hole. It's the mouth of a cave!" shouted another.

Gradually, the entrance to the cave grew wide enough for a man to walk through. Torches were lit and the men began to file in.

"There's the lake the boy talked about," whispered one of Gwrtheyrn's workmen.

"What's that snoring noise?" quavered another.

As the torchlight reflected off the waters of the lake, Gwrtheyrn and his followers saw the outline of a huge white dragon sleeping on a rocky ledge at one end of the lake. On a similar ledge at the other end of the lake a large red dragon lay fast asleep.

"Come away," whispered the king. "It's too dangerous to stay here. And be careful. Don't make the slightest sound or you'll wake these dragons."

Warily they all crept out of the cave mouth.

"We'd better close this hole after us and let the

dragons fight their battles in private," suggested Gwrtheyrn.

"Certainly not!"

Everyone turned to look at the boy once more.

"Myrddin Emrys, have you any more advice to give us?" asked the king.

"Make the hole bigger," said the boy. "Big enough for a dragon to fly out. Then we'll have to wait till night time."

By this time no one doubted the boy's word. The wise men slunk into the shadows of the trees and were never seen again. The hole was enlarged and everyone in the camp waited for night.

"But what is the explanation for all this?" Gwrtheyrn asked the wise boy.

"Those creatures in the cave are more than just dragons," said Myrddin Emrys. "The red dragon represents the Old Welsh who have lived in these lands for hundreds and hundreds of years. We are a civilised people with our own culture and religion. The white dragon, on the other hand, represents those wild, savage and godless people who are trying to steal our lands from us."

"Hors and Hengist and their mob!" whispered one of Gwrtheyrn's soldiers.

"Yes, the Saxons. The men of the long knives,"

said Myrddin. "The two dragons will fight in this lake till one has defeated the other. When one dragon has yielded, then you will have peace to build your castle on this spot."

At that moment, a terrible roar came from the depths of the cave. The dragons had woken up and were at each other's throats. Soon the hills were shaking and everyone knew that a bloody battle was taking place in the underground lake.

The screams of the dragons and a puff or two of smoke issued from the mouth of the cave. The ground shook for most of the night as the dragons flung each other against the underground rocks.

Then, shortly before dawn, the men heard one of the creatures approach the exit hole in the side of the hill. With one long screech, an injured white dragon flew out of the cave and took wing over the mountaintops. It flew towards the rising sun and the lands of the east.

"That dragon will never return to the mountains of Snowdonia," said Myrddin Emrys. "The red dragon owns this land for evermore!"

The king was so relieved, he announced that he would give the plot of land to the boy. "You can build your own castle here," he said.

And that's what happened. The fort that was

built there was called 'Dinas Emrys'. That is still its name today.

King Gwrtheyrn went in search of another safe site for his castle. After looking high and low, he came to a lonely valley on the Llŷn Peninsula. And do you what the name of that place is? Gwrtheyrn's Stream or Nant Gwrtheyrn!

And to this day the red dragon is the coat of arms of the Welsh – to remind us of that long-ago dragon who kept the land of Wales safe from the white dragon's men.

Welsh Women 1
Dwynwen

The patron saint of Welsh lovers

Welsh Women 2
Marged

The strong woman of Snowdonia

Welsh Women 3
Mary Jones

And her Bible quest

Welsh Women 4
Gwenllian

The warrior princess

Welsh Women 5
Jemima Nicholas

Heroine of the Fishguard
invasion

Welsh Women 6
Melangell

Friend of the Hares

www.carreg-gwalch.com